Cow Tales

Paintings & Poems by
Linda Coddington

inda Coddington

This book belongs to

_____

PALMETTO
PUBLISHING
Charleston, SC
www.PalmettoPublishing.com

Cow Tales
Copyright © 2022 by Linda Coddington

First Edition

Hardcover ISBN: 979-8-8229-0619-8
Paperback ISBN: 979-8-8229-0618-1

Cow Tales

A collection of bovine rhymes

Brutus gets himself in trouble
everywhere he goes.
Bo is learning patience
from the monarch on his nose.

Rosey loves her flowers;
Chase loves flowers too.
Rosey likes their colors;
Chase just likes to chew!

Val is such a special gal.
She's beautiful and kind.
Minnie wears a bonnet
that someone left behind.

Fancy watches horses
as they race around the track.
Sunny has a lot of friends
and they all want a snack!

Betsy has a flag and bow
of red and white and blue.
ALL of them have stories
they can't wait to share with YOU!

Linda Coddington
4 22

Minnie

Mrs. Farmer had a bonnet;
how I loved it so.
She'd wear it in the garden
when she'd shovel, rake, and hoe.

One day when she went inside,
she left it by the shed.
I hurried over, dipped my neck,
and scooped it on my head!

I felt so grand in my new hat;
so full of joy and pride.
But then, quite unexpectedly,
she reappeared outside.

There I stood, caught red-hooved,
feeling rather meek.
But Mrs. Farmer only laughed
and kissed me on the cheek.

6

Linda Coddington

Brutus

I didn't mean to do it!
I couldn't help myself.
The flowers were so pretty
just sitting on the shelf.

I only wanted a little sniff.
Well... maybe a nibble or two.
But now, just look what I have done!
Oh, what am I to do?

Grandma saw the broken pot
and dirt upon the sill.
But, even as she frowned at me,
she said, "I love you still."

8

Linda Coddington

Bo

I see this little butterfly
drying out his wings.
I know he cannot wait to fly
and explore so many things.

But as I watch, he tries to go
and lands upon my nose!
It tickles me! I wish he'd fly.
(He's nervous, I suppose.)

So I'll be very gentle.
I'll hold my head so steady.
I'll sit here very patiently
until he's sure he's ready.

Even if it takes all day,
I know that in the end,
he'll be very thankful
I was such a loving friend.

Linda Coddington

Fancy

I watch a young horse running
in the field just over there.
I hear his pounding hooves and
see the wind blow through his hair.

I'd really love to run with him
but I can't keep his pace.
I heard Farmer Henry say
he's training for a race.

So I'll be there to cheer him on;
you can be sure of that!
I'll be the only cow there
in a fancy derby hat.

12

Linda Coddington
2022

Rosey

Flowers are my favorite thing.
Pansies! Roses! Clover!
Any time I see them near
I have to mosey over.

Their colors make me happy.
I think I'll pick a few.
Pink and yellow. Orange and red.
They come in every hue.

But I would never eat them.
I'm not that kind of cow.
I'd much prefer to wear them
like a crown upon my brow.

Linda Coddington
2022

14

Chase

A floral wreath. What a great idea!
But, no - I beg to differ!
Flowers are not safe, you see,
when so close to my sniffer.

They smelled so very tasty;
I had to try a bite.
But then I ate them all!
Though I knew it wasn't right.

So now my belly aches.
Can you hear it churn?
Daddy asks me as I groan,
"What lesson did you learn?"

16

Linda Coddington

Val

Some folks say I'm beautiful.
As pretty as a rose.
Others say it looks as though
there's pepper on my nose.

But Momma always tells me
when I'm older I will find
that, while beauty may be nice,
it's more important to be kind.

So always lend a helping hoof
to anyone in need.
Treating others as yourself
is most important. Yes, indeed!

18

Linda Coddington

Betsy

I hear the music playing.
They'll be here really soon.
The drums are getting louder.
Hey, I recognize that tune!

I see the fife and drum corps.
Oh, I can hardly wait!
So I walk around the barn
and then I slip right through the gate.

I get in line behind the band;
match my hoof-steps to the beat.
It only takes a little while
until we reach Main Street.

I can't believe it's finally here -
this day for which I've prayed.
See me with my bow and flag?
I'm part of the parade!

Howdy neighbor! How are you?
Do you like to play?
Why don't you come over
and stay a while today?

Mr. Goat tells funny jokes
sure to make you giggle.
Penny Pig will dance for you.
She'll jump and stomp and wiggle.

Bob the horse would love to give you
rides upon his back.
By the way, could you maybe
bring us all a snack?

We like carrots, corn, and apples,
grass and lettuce, too.
But mostly we all love to play
with new friends just like you.

Thanks for hanging out with us,
and listening as we rhyme.
Turn back to the beginning,
and we'll do it one more time!

About the Author

It all started with one cow.
Then two, then three, then four.
I was having so much fun
I painted even more.

I'd visit them at the dairy farm
near where I grew up.
Some were skittish and sort of shy.
Some were playful as a pup.

But all of them are beautiful;
their eyes just melt my heart.
I didn't know that painting them
was only just the start.

Stories started taking shape;
the rhymes came in a rush.
Words flowed across the paper
like the paint beneath my brush.

Rhyming books were my favorite
when I was just a kid.
I thought about my grandkids,
so this is what I did.

I put them both together;
the paintings and the pages.
Hoping this book brings a smile
to children of all ages.

Dedicated to Chase, Ellie, Luke, Jonah, Zachariah, and Gabriel

~Special thanks~

The Stoltzfus family: Thank you for allowing me to come hang out at Pennwood Farms and play with your cows! Allen Lehman, thanks for sharing your incredible photos of "Brutus" and "Rosey".

My family: When I doubt, you believe...

Lightning Source UK Ltd.
Milton Keynes UK
UKHW050617221122
412603UK00010B/163

9 798822 906181